Creative PROBLEM SOLVING
FOR KIDS

DL 95

Grades 5 - 8

Written by **Dianne Draze**
Illustrated by **Amber Tornquist**

Edited by **Sonsie Conroy**

ISBN 1-883055-03-2

© Copyright 1994 Dandy Lion Publications
All rights reserved. Purchase of this book gives the purchaser the right to duplicate copies of pages bearing copyright information in limited quantities for classroom use. Reproduction for an entire school or school system is not allowed without written permission from the publisher. Duplication by any means for commercial purposes is strictly forbidden.

Published by **Dandy Lion Publications**
    P.O. Box 190
    San Luis Obispo, CA 93406

Table of Contents

Information for the Instructor

What is Creative Problem Solving?

Creative Problem Solving (CPS) is a process that allows people to apply both creative and rational thinking to find solutions to everyday problems. Creative Problem Solving can eliminate the tendency to approach problems in a haphazard manner and, consequently, prevents surprises and/or disappointment with the solution. It is both a way to enhance creative behavior and also a systematic way of organizing information and ideas in order to solve problems. It uses both convergent and divergent thinking. Students who learn the principles of CPS develop a sense of control in their lives derived from their ability to deal with difficult situations creatively.

Instructional Objectives

Instructors using **Creative Problem Solving for Kids** to train their students in the Creative Problem Solving process will be providing for the following skills:

- The ability to read or hear a passage and select relevant information.
- The ability to analyze social situations.
- The ability to think creatively to generate a large number of possibilities (fluency).
- The ability to think creatively to generate a variety of different possibilities (flexibility).
- The ability to generate criteria for judging.
- The ability to evaluate options based on given criteria (evaluation).
- The ability to apply creative thinking to a variety of situations.
- The ability to plan activities that are relevant to accomplishing a goal.

Presenting CPS

It is advisable to introduce Creative Problem Solving procedures to students in a group lesson, having students pool ideas and recording these ideas on large sheets of paper or on an overhead transparency. As students become more familiar with the process, they may work on problems either in small groups or individually. Each step of the CPS process is introduced in this book by lessons that teach the necessary skills for that particular stage and that give alternate procedures to use at that stage. Additionally, there are several practice problems that can be used in large-group instruction before asking students to apply the CPS process to a personal problem.

This book offers several different vehicles for presenting CPS and teaching the skills that are used in CPS. These include:

- **Teaching Notes** - This section includes a brief description of each stage of CPS as well as key questions and lessons.
- **Skill Builders** - These pages teach skills that are needed to master each stage.
- **Worksheets** - These pages are open frames that students can use to apply CPS to their own problems.
- **Practice Problems** - The worksheets for these four problems take students step-by-step through the CPS process so they can see the entire process applied to a problem from beginning to end.
- **Pocket Problem Solver** - This form condenses all the steps in CPS into a three-page format.

The CPS Process

1. Sensing Problems

Creative Problem Solving is a six-step process. In starting with the first step, students must first select a problem. This involves identifying a perplexing situation or a problem that needs solving. Usually people have more problems than they know what to do with, so it is a matter of selecting the most pressing problem. Sometimes though, people need some help in defining a problem that needs solving. There may be a vague sense of imbalance or uneasiness, but the person may not be able to pinpoint the exact nature of the problem. In this situation, it is most helpful to list all the facts and feelings that are associated with the area of concern. In looking for a problem, one can either focus on **obstacles** (things that need to be removed) or **outcomes** (things you want to attain).

When the problem situation has been generally defined, the students may proceed with the following five steps in the CPS process.

2. Finding Facts

In this step, students find all the important, relevant facts that relate to the problem. If not enough information is known, students must ask questions that will result in additional information. They make note of factual information, observations, feelings, impressions or inferences, and questions. They look at both what they already know and what they need to find out.

3. Defining the Problem

In this step, students make several problem statements in an attempt to define the "real problem." This is a time to analyze the situation and try to get a better understanding of the entire problem. They look at the problem from several different perspectives and write different "how to" problem statements. The statements should be brief and should lead to many different ideas in the next stage of the process.

The most common way to generate problem statements is to complete the statement "*In what ways might I/we...*" All statements generated in this step should include **ownership** (who is involved?) and **action** (what do they want to do?).

4. Finding Ideas

After selecting the best problem statement, students then think of as many ideas or alternatives as they can to solve the problem. Without analyzing ideas, they try to generate a large number of unusual, unique, creative ideas. They do not think about whether the ideas are good or bad or whether they could work or not. They just try to write down as many ideas as possible. Only after they have created a long list do they select those ideas that seem most workable.

5. Judging Ideas

In this step, students choose the most useful idea. To do this, they first determine appropriate evaluative criteria. Then they use these criteria to systematically rate each idea. Once all ideas are rated, students look at the ideas and their ratings and try to find the one best solution — the idea that best meets all the tests or rules. While students are looking for the one best idea, they also need to consider whether two ideas could be combined to make one superior solution or if one idea could be changed in some way to make it a better solution.

6. Taking Action

In the last step of the process, students outline a plan of action for implementing the idea(s) selected. They consider sources of assistance and potential problems. They make a list of short-term and long-term activities. They also state how they will know if their idea was successful. With this last question, the CPS process becomes a continuing cycle of evaluating where you are and how you can progress to the next level.

Introducing Creative Problem Solving

Creative Problem Solving can be an intense, thought-provoking process. While the end result is always preferable to the haphazard way most people make decisions and solve problems, it is, nonetheless, something that children will appreciate more if they see the benefit and overall scheme before they begin learning each skill.

Before introducing the Creative Problem Solving process, it is good to set the stage by discussing problems that children commonly face and how they typically solve these problems. As you discuss the student's problems, make a list on the board of the problems they suggest. Although children usually have more than an adequate number of problems to share, if they are reluctant to share problems or have trouble thinking of problems, you might use the following prompts to initiate the discussion:

- things you want to change
- relationships with other people
- obstacles you want to overcome
- situations that don't work out the way you want
- how to deal with peer pressure
- how to get what you want
- how to find out something you want to know
- a dilemma
- things about yourself you want to improve
- finding a better way to...
- improving a product
- resolving differences between expectations from other people and what you want to do

When you are finished, keep this list as you may wish to use these problems later as examples in presenting each step in the process.

At this point, you can tell students that you are going to teach them a process for solving problems. This process requires both creative thinking and critical thinking. Once they have learned the process, they will be better able to handle big problems, small problems and the ambiguous situations that cause us to feel uncomfortable but we're not sure why we feel this way or what to do about it. Briefly present the creative problem solving process as presented on page 8.

Creative Problem Solving

Sensing Problems

Decide what problem situations exist and which one problem
is important enough to warrant your time and energy

Finding Facts

Record and sort out information about the situation

Defining the Problem

Analyze the situation and define the "real problem"

Finding Ideas

Think of many creative ways to solve the problem

Judging Ideas

Use criteria to select the best idea

Taking Action

Plan how to implement the solution

© 1994 Dandy Lion - C. P. S. for Kids

Sensing Problems

This first stage of Creative Problem Solving is a springboard for the rest of the process. Students will be looking carefully at all their experiences and concerns in order to discover problem areas that they would like to explore. It is a way of looking over the entire universe and focusing in on those things that they find personally troubling or interesting, the injustices they want to correct, the obstacles they want to overcome, or the things they want to change. This stage is for contemplating what general area interests them enough to devote some time and thought to solving the problem.

Many children have very clear ideas of what things are problems in their lives. If this is the case, it is not necessary to devote a lot of time to this stage. You can quickly state the problem area and go on to the Finding Facts stage and begin recording all the information about the chosen problem. At other times, however, people may just have an uneasy feeling that things are not quite right. They may also feel that they want to do something but are not sure where to direct their efforts. In these cases, the problem solving process, must start at the Sensing Problems stage.

When looking for problem situations, it is sometimes helpful to think in terms of **outcomes** and **obstacles**. Outcomes are the goals or end results that you hope for. They are the things that finish the statement, "Wouldn't it be nice if..." The other way to ferret out problems is to think about obstacles. These are the things that prevent people from achieving a desired goal.

There are two other things to consider when selecting a problem. They are **ownership** and **influence**. Whatever situation the students are considering, they should be in the position to be able to do something about the problem. If the problem belongs to someone else, it is up to the other person to initiate a solution.

Questions

You can use the following questions and sentence fragments to help students sense situations they want to change or problems they want to solve.

1. If I could do anything I would...
2. What do you want?
3. I wonder if we/I could...
4. I wish...
5. What fears or weakness do you want to overcome?
6. Wouldn't it be nice if...
7. What would make you really happy?
8. What bothers you?
9. If you had a magic wand, how would you use it?
10. What could you make a difference by doing?
11. What do you feel passionately about?
12. When you listen to the news, what strikes you most?
13. What is something you worry about?

Lessons and Teaching Suggestions

1. Current Events Problems

Divide the class into groups and give each group a newspaper and several news magazines. Ask them to read the headlines and make note of the problems that are associated with the headlines. They should look for situations that need to be changed or problems that need to be solved.

After each group has made a list of several problems, have the groups share their problems with the whole class. On a big piece of poster paper, record the problems.

2. Wish List

Tell students to pretend that they can make wishes and have those wishes come true. Ask them to think of the following wishes and write them down:

- a wish for themselves
- a wish for their families
- a wish for their city
- a wish for their country
- a wish for the world

Have them look at their wish lists and decide if any of these wishes could be topics for creative problem solving. In other words, is there something on this list that, if they used creative thinking and hard work, they could make a reality?

3. Personal Problems

Explain that sometimes we know exactly what our problem is. It could be a younger brother who gets into our personal possessions, a class in school that we find particularly difficult, or a dispute with a classmate. Sometimes, however, we just have a vague feeling that something is not right. At those times, we need to look a little deeper to find out what is bothering us. The better we are able to identify our feelings and define our problems, the more control we have in our lives.

Use the worksheet entitled "Identifying Personal Problems" to help students identify things in their lives they would like to change. After they have completed the worksheet, have them select one concern or situation that they would be interested in improving.

4. Improvements

Materials: Several different kinds of toothbrushes showing different designs or improvements

Explain that sometime you can find problems by thinking about what things need to be improved. This is how many of our product innovations occur. A toothbrush manufacturer will look at its product and say, "What can we do to improve this plain old toothbrush?" They start thinking and before long they have toothbrushes that are different colors, have different shapes and configurations of bristles, are angled, or have designs on them. Display the different kinds of toothbrushes. Discuss other changes that students have noticed in toothbrushes.

Continue to explain that other times someone may notice a problem with a product and set out to overcome the problem. It could be someone who gets tired of not being able to see where he is going when he is using an umbrella or someone who finds the common shovel to be lacking in modern qualities.

Ask students to look around their environment for a couple of days and notice things that they think need improving. They can keep track of the items that are in need of improvement on a large piece of poster paper that is mounted on a wall of the classroom or by using the worksheet entitled "Improvements."

5. Webbing

Explain that often when you choose a situation for problem solving, it is too large or too vague. For instance, if you chose the topic of "crime," this problem has many ramifications and related issues. It would be impossible to tackle the entire problem of crime. A better procedure is to analyze the problem and graphically lay out all the many parts. You can then choose a part of this larger topic to solve.

Choose a large topic like "school," "our town," "gangs," "pollution," "censorship," or some other topic.

Write the topic in a circle in the middle of the board or a large piece of paper. As students raise various issues related to this general topic, write them on lines that branch out from this central circle. As ideas are shared that are related to things that have already been recorded, write them on lines that branch out from the existing lines.

Once the topic has been explored, show students how they can then select one aspect, like "ozone depletion," "behavior in the lunch room," or "study skills" for further exploration. Use the worksheet on page 13 to use this procedure on an individual or small group basis.

6. People - Places - Procedures - Things

One way to find problems worth solving is by looking in various **places** (home, class, school, neighborhood), analyzing how **people** get along, reviewing what **procedures** need changing, or looking for **things** that need improving.

Divide students into small groups and have each group construct a chart that is divided into 4 sections, each section labeled either *people*, *places*, *procedures*, or *things*. Ask them to use these words as cues and write ideas for problems they think need solving in each section of the chart.

7. Defining Your Own Problems

If your intent is just to instruct students in and give them practice in CPS, you may want to skip this first step initially and provide them with problems. You can use the problems that are defined in our companion book, *Pickles, Problems and Dilemmas*. You can also define your own problems. Some suggestions for problems are:

1. **Resolving problems at home** like scheduling, disputes between individuals, how to handle responsibilities.
2. Solutions for problems presented in **literature**.
3. Finding a way to deal with **typical classroom situations** like cheating, teasing, bullying, losing athletic equipment, failing to return library books, keeping the room clean, or getting to the bus on time; as well as more serious problems like truancy, lack of funding, or violence.
4. **Making plans** for a club, hideout, or party.
5. Coming up with ideas for **special projects** (for school, scouts, 4-H, holidays, or ways to show someone you care about them).
6. Solving **family problems** like fighting with siblings, getting chores done, not having a private place, or deciding which TV program to watch.
7. **Fulfilling needs** like new tennis shoes, help with math, or more freedom to make your own decisions.
8. Solving **logistical problems** such as how to get together with friends who live across town, how to get a large science project to school or how to move a large rock from its present location.
9. Tackling **current social problems** like gangs, prejudice, homelessness, child or spouse abuse, sexual harassment, substance abuse, or unemployment.
10. Resolving **value conflicts** such as what to do when you find a wallet full of money, whether to go to a play with your parents or a movie with a friend, or whether to spend your allowance on a new toy or buy your sister a birthday present.
11. Dealing with situations **when things do not go as you had planned** such as losing your only bus token, forgetting your lunch, getting on the wrong bus, or finding that the movie you came to see is not playing.
12. Taking on **environmental problems** that deal with pollution, endangered species, depletion of resources, and ozone depletion.
13. Pondering how to solve **serious national problems** like the national debt, poverty, public safety, national defense, industrial growth or decline, censorship, and public health.

Name _____

Looking For Problems

Here are some places or topics where you might find problems that need solutions. As you think of problems in these areas that you would like to do something about, write them in the appropriate spaces.

Home Problems

School Problems

Environmental Problems

National Problems

World Problems

Social Problems

Other Problems

© 1994 Dandy Lion - C. P. S. for Kids

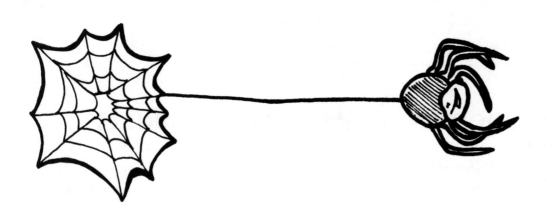

Sensing Problems

Name _____

Webbing for Ideas

Write your problem in the center circle. Record all aspects about this problem on lines that are attached to the circle. Write ideas that are related on connecting lines.

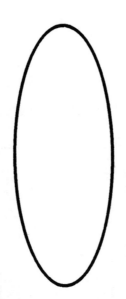

© 1994 Dandy Lion - C.P.S. for Kids

Name _____

Identifying Personal Problems

Sometimes problems are things in your life that you would like to happen or things you would like to change for the better. Sometimes they are situations that make you unhappy or dissatisfied. Finish these statements and you'll discover some problems in your personal life you can solve.

1. I feel frustrated when _____

2. I don't like it when_____

3. A problem I have with other people is _____

4. I get really angry when _____

5. At my home I would like to change _____

6. The thing that worries me most is _____

7. One thing I would like to accomplish is _____

8. If I didn't have to worry about failure I would_____

9. If I had more time I would _____

10. I would like to overcome _____

11. _____ stresses me out.

                                        © 1994 Dandy Lion - C. P. S. for Kids

Name _____

Group Problem Finding

If you and your group are looking for a problem to solve, it is sometimes helpful to ask some probing questions. The following questions will help you uncover problems that you can solve.

1. What is being wasted or depleted?_____

2. What is unfair? _____

3. What needs reorganizing?_____

4. What problems are related to people not getting along with each other? _____

_____

5. What takes too long?_____

6. What costs too much? _____

7. What needs do people your age have? _____

8. What things are changing for the worse? _____

9. What misunderstandings exist?_____

10. What is too complicated? _____

11. What is inefficient? _____

Name _____

Improvements

Keep track of things you use around your school and your home that need improving. After you have made a long list, choose one thing that you think you could improve.

These things need improving   Why?

_____   _____

_____   _____

_____   _____

_____   _____

_____   _____

_____   _____

_____   _____

_____   _____

_____   _____

_____   _____

_____   _____

_____   _____

The thing I want to improve is _____

         © 1994 Dandy Lion - C. P. S. for Kids

Finding Facts

The Finding Facts stage is designed to increase students' awareness of the problem area they have selected. If the problem-solver did not start with a search for a problem, but instead started with a definite problem that he or she wanted to solve, the problem-solving process would start at this point by writing down everything he or she knows or needs to know about the situation.

Students should write down all the information, facts, feelings, impressions, opinions, and questions that are related to the problem situation. Once they have randomly written down everything they can think of, they should sort out the information, noting what information has special significance and what information is still needed.

Questions

Questions to use at this stage include:
1. What are all the things you know about this situation?
2. Who is involved?
3. What has already been done?
4. What information is the most important (must know) and what information is helpful but not necessary?
5. What are some additional things you might need to know before you could solve this problem?
6. Where could you find the answers to these questions?

Lessons and Teaching Suggestions

1. Newspaper Facts

Give students an article from a newspaper or a news magazine. Choose one that relates to a potential or existing problem. Have them read the article and then as a group list the most important information contained in the article.

2. Defining a Broad Topic

Give students a broad topic like "drugs," "recess," "school lunches," "sports programs in our community," or "staying healthy." As a group, list information about the situation. Once all the facts have been recorded, highlight the most important ones.

3. Act It Out

Choose a situation that is relevant to most students. Have two or more students act out the situation in such a way that they are discussing the problem from two different perspectives. After the skit, the rest of the class should record all the information related to this situation that they could derive from watching the skit and decide what additional information they would like to know about this situation that was not presented in the skit.

4. Literature Selection

Choose a selection from literature in which the character(s) is facing a problem. Have students read the selection and list everything that the author has told the reader about the character and the problem. Then have them pretend that they are in the character's place and determine what additional information they would like to have in order to be able to solve the problem.

Name _____

Package Problem

Here is a package that you have just received. What things do you know about the package by just looking at it from the outside?

_____

_____

_____

_____

_____

_____

_____

_____

_____

_____

_____

What else would you need to know before you could guess what is inside?

_____

_____

_____

_____

                    © 1994 Dandy Lion - C. P. S. for Kids

Name _____

Improving the Math Book

The publisher of your math book has just come to you and asked for your help. They are going to improve your math book, and they want your suggestions. You should start by making a list of things that you know about the book. Write factual information as well as opinions and impressions.

_____

_____

_____

_____

_____

_____

_____

_____

_____

_____

_____

_____

_____

_____

Put a * by the information that most relates to the problem of improving the book.

Name _____

Comic Editor

Your new job is going to be great. You are the editor for the comics page of your local newspaper. One of your first tasks will be to evaluate the page and make suggestions for improvements. Get a comics page from your newspaper and write all the information you can think of. Write opinions and impressions as well as facts.

_____

_____

_____

_____

_____

_____

_____

_____

_____

_____

_____

_____

Put a * by the information that you think is most important to your job of improving this page.

© 1994 Dandy Lion - C. P. S. for Kids

Name _____

Listing Facts

Use this page to record everything you know about
your problem.

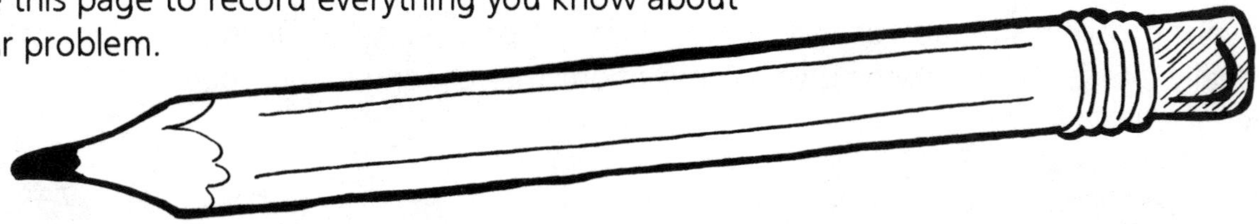

Problem Situation _____

_____

This is what I know about the problem situation.

_____

_____

_____

_____

_____

_____

_____

_____

_____

_____

I would like to have this additional information.

_____

_____

_____

Put a * by the most important information.

Name _____

Real Versus Ideal

Think of your problem situation as having two different parts — what really exists and what should ideally exist. Write everything you know about the real and ideal aspects of this situation.

Problem Situation _____

What is

What ideally should be

_____   _____
_____   _____
_____   _____
_____   _____
_____   _____
_____   _____
_____   _____
_____   _____
_____   _____
_____   _____

© 1994 Dandy Lion - C. P. S. for Kids

Name _____

Different Points of View

Most problems have more than one side. By considering the different points of view, you will be better able to understand the problem and then solve it. Use this page to identify two different viewpoints about your problem.

Problem Situation _____

```
_____'s Viewpoint              _____'s Viewpoint

_____              _____

_____              _____

_____              _____

_____              _____

_____              _____

_____              _____

_____              _____
```

Additional Facts

_____

_____

_____

_____

_____

_____

_____

Name _____

Just the Facts

Write all the facts related to your problem by answering the following questions.

Who? _____

_____

_____

_____

What? _____

_____

_____

_____

_____

Where? _____

_____

When? _____

_____

Why? _____

_____

_____

How? _____

_____

What has been tried so far? _____

_____

Put a * by the most important information.

© 1994 Dandy Lion - C. P. S. for Kids

Defining the Problem

This step requires students to review the important information they outlined in the Finding Facts stage. Then they must think creatively to pose several possible problem statements. Explain to students that sometimes the problem is not what appears on the surface. Sometimes by stating the problem in several different ways they will be able to find a way to look at the problem that will allow them to come up with more ideas than they thought possible.

The problem statements should be as broad and diverse as possible. The most common way to generate problem statements is to complete the sentence fragments "In what ways might I/we...?" *(IWWMW...)* or "How to...?" Another approach is to think of the problem as people taking some action. In this case, you would use the sentence structure "who might do what." An explanation below shows how you can break the problem down into its components and then use this structure to pose several different problem statements.

Once students have listed a number of possible problem statements, they must select the best one. That is, they want to choose the statement that will allow them to generate a large number of solutions in the Finding Ideas stage.

Questions

Questions at this step might include:

1. What is the real problem?
2. Can you state the problem a different way?
3. How else could you view this problem?
4. What are you really trying to do?
5. How would other people view this problem?
6. How could you...? (finish in as many different ways as you can)
7. What do you want to accomplish?
8. Why?

Lessons and Teaching Suggestions

1. Practice Problem

Take the example of the girl who wants a new dress for the dance but does not have enough money to purchase a new dress. She could look at her situation in a very limited way and, therefore, limit her options for solutions or her problem could be stated in the following ways, giving her more options. Give students the worksheet on page 28. Read through the facts. Have students pose several different problem statements. Some possible statements are:

- In what ways might I get a new dress for the dance?
- In what ways might I look nice for the dance?
- In what ways might I impress my date?
- In what ways might I earn the money I need to purchase a dress?
- In what ways might I find a dress that doesn't cost so much?
- In what ways might I enlist my parent's help?
- In what ways might I get a dress that doesn't cost anything?
- In what ways might I change the dress requirements for the dance so I don't have to get a new dress?
- In what ways might I remake a dress I already own?

When they have finished listing possible problem statements, have students choose the one problem statement that will best define the problem and allow them to generate a number of solutions.

If additional practice is needed, give students the situation of someone being teased by other students because he is overweight. His problem might be stated as:

- How can I get the other kids to stop teasing me?
- How can I lose weight?
- How can I get the other kids to recognize my good qualities?

Have students add other problem statements.

2. Who - Do - What?

Practice writing problem statements by using the "who - action verb - what" format. Select a problem situation. If necessary, generate a list of information. Then make a list of people involved in the problem, a list of possible actions, and a list of objects of the action. For a problem of saving paper in the school, your list might look like this:

Who	Action Verbs
teachers	reuse
parents	recycle
students	streamline
custodians	contribute
principal	use
	encourage
	eliminate

What
savings
art projects
assignments
chalk board
resources
paper

The problem statements would take the form "How can (who) (action verb) (what)? Some possible statements for this situation might be:

- How can principals encourage savings?
- How can teachers eliminate assignments?
- How can teachers streamline assignments?
- How can students reuse paper?
- How can parents contribute resources?
- How can teachers substitute art project materials?
- How can custodians recycle paper?

- How can teachers use chalk boards in place of paper?

3. Classroom Problem

Select a classroom problem like passing in papers, losing athletic equipment, teasing, keeping the room clean, or something else that everyone in the class can identify with. Make a list of facts associated with the problem (Finding Facts) and then write several problem statements using the IWWM... or Who-Do-What format. When you have finished writing several problem statements, select the one that will give you the best opportunity to brainstorm solutions.

4. Different Viewpoint

Show students that sometimes looking at a different, point of view can give them an opportunity to see the problem in a different light and come up with different, more creative problem statements. Take the situation of dirty bathrooms in the school. The following different perspectives might generate these problem statements:

Students
- How can we avoid the rush of people in the bathroom at recess?
- How can we make the bathrooms more attractive?
- How can we avoid being blamed for the problem?

Principal
- How can we regulate student use?
- How can we monitor student use?
- How can we reward students for keeping the bathrooms clean?

Teacher
- How can we teach students to be more responsible?
- How can we instill pride in the physical appearance of the school?

Custodian

- How can I keep up with the mess?
- How can we install equipment that will eliminate some of the mess?
- How can I get someone to help me clean?

Choose another problem that students can uniformly relate to and have them look at the situation from a couple of different perspectives and write problem statements from those perspectives.

5. Combining Problem Statements

Many times when students have finished writing their problem statements, they will find that there are a couple of statements that are similar. In these cases, instead of choosing one statement, they can combine the statements to form one improved statement.

An example might be the following list of problem statements for a situation in which a young person is not doing well in math class.

1. In what ways might I avoid taking any more math?
2. In what ways might I get help?
3. In what ways might I better understand this material?
4. In what ways might I put myself in a situation that will be easier?
5. In what ways might I get along with my math teacher better?
6. In what ways might I find the time I need to study math more?

This student may choose to combine numbers 2 and 3 and write a problem statement that says, "In what ways might I get help to better understand this material?"

If you have done some of the practice lessons above, go back and look at your lists of problem statements. Ask if any of the statements can be combined to make a better problem statement than was originally selected.

Name _____

Dance Dress

Read the following information about Rachel's problem. Try to think of several different ways to state her problem. Write as many ways as you can.

Rachel has been asked to go to the winter formal with David. She has never gone out with David before and would like to make a favorable impression. The winter formal is usually a semi-formal affair. Rachel would like a new dress, but dresses usually cost about $100 and she only has $25. Her parents say that they will not buy her a new dress. They cannot afford that much money for something she would wear only one night. Rachel has an older sister and an older cousin who have several dresses that they have worn to dances, but neither girl is the same size as Rachel. Rachel has a job baby-sitting for about 5 hours every week. The dance is in 2 weeks.

Rachel's problem can be stated as:

How can _____

How can _____

How can _____

How can _____

How can _____

How can _____

How can _____

                                           © 1994 Dandy Lion - C. P. S. for Kids

Name _____

Lost Lunches

Room 10 has a problem. Everyone, except the people who buy hot lunches, leaves their lunches on a bench in the back of the room by the coats in the morning. Every day for the past two weeks people have found that various items have been missing from their lunches by lunch time. No one will admit to stealing the items out of the lunches. Miss Prim, the teacher, has admonished the class that this is not a socially acceptable thing to do and that if the thief is caught, punishment will be administered. Still, the thievery continues. No one is allowed to stay in the classroom when Miss Prim is not in there. The people who keep losing parts of their lunches (usually the best parts) are getting very aggravated.

The class has decided to think creatively about a solution. Help them think of several different approaches to this problem.

In what ways might _____

In what ways might _____

In what ways might _____

In what ways might _____

In what ways might _____

In what ways might _____

In what ways might _____

In what ways might _____

Name _____

Defining the Problem

In order to successfully solve problems, you need to be able to look at the problem in several different ways. Look through the important facts you have written about your problem. Think about what the "real problem" might be. Write as many different ideas as you can by completing this sentence in many different ways.

In what ways might _____ ?

In what ways might _____ ?

In what ways might _____ ?

In what ways might _____ ?

In what ways might _____ ?

In what ways might _____ ?

In what ways might _____ ?

In what ways might _____ ?

In what ways might _____ ?

In what ways might _____ ?

Choose the statement that you think best describes the problem.

The real problem is _____

                                            © 1994 Dandy Lion - C. P. S. for Kids

Defining the Problem

Name _____

What's the Real Problem?

Now that you have written all you know about the problem and collected any additional information you need, you need to decide what you real problem is before you can really get into solving it. Use this page to analyze your problem. Try to describe your problem in may different ways.

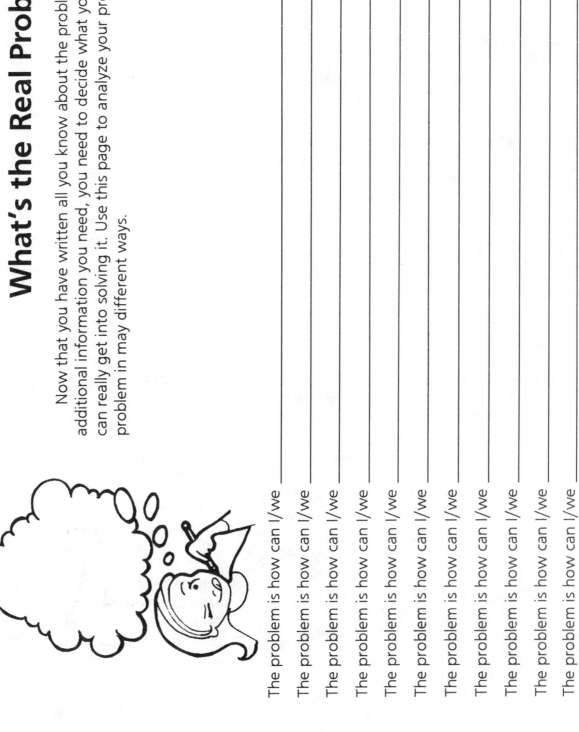

The problem is how can I/we _____

The problem is how can I/we _____

The problem is how can I/we _____

The problem is how can I/we _____

The problem is how can I/we _____

The problem is how can I/we _____

The problem is how can I/we _____

The problem is how can I/we _____

The problem is how can I/we _____

The problem is how can I/we _____

The problem is how can I/we _____

Finding Ideas

The Finding Ideas stage is the phase for freewheeling, creative thinking. The problem statement has been selected, and now it is time to think about all the ways this problem can be solved. The goal is to generate as many ideas as possible, because you have a greater likelihood of producing a good solution if you have many ideas to choose from than if you only have a few selections. Once a lot of ideas have been recorded, the best solution (or the best combination of several solutions) will be selected in the next phase, Judging Ideas.

At this stage you want to encourage students to think as freely and creatively as possible. Rather than judging ideas, they should try to think of as many unusual ideas as possible. While some ideas may not be usable, they may trigger other ideas that are worthwhile.

Questions

Questions you could use to encourage creative thinking during this stage are:

1. What are all the ideas you can think of?
2. Does that idea make you think of any other ideas?
3. What else comes to mind?
4. Can you get any ideas by thinking about something in nature?
5. Can you get any ideas by thinking about...?
6. What can you use in another way?
7. What can you change in some way?
8. What can be made bigger, stronger, greater, higher, longer, thicker, or more intense?
9. What can be made smaller, lower, weaker, shorter, lighter, or more streamlined?
10. What can you substitute?
11. How can you rearrange things?
12. What could be turned around, upside down, backwards, or inside out?
13. What can you combine?

Lessons and Teaching Suggestions

1. Warm-ups

If students have not had a lot of experience with creative thinking, it is a good idea to get their creative juices flowing with some warm-up exercises. These can be done as a whole class, individually or in small groups. Encourage off-beat, unusual answers. The following are some ideas for stimulating creative thinking:

- What tastes happy?
- What does blue smell like?
- How can you catch a smile?
- What if animals could talk?
- What if snow was colored?
- What if we had two moons?
- Name all the things that are hard and green.
- Name all the things that are useful and round.
- Name all the things that are valuable and would fit in your pocket.
- What are all the uses for half-used erasers?
- What are all the uses for empty milk cartons?
- What are some ideas for changing your chair?
- What are all the ways you can think of to attach two things together?

2. Brainstorming

Brainstorming is the most commonly used technique for producing a large number of ideas. It is usually done in a small group. Members of the group freely record their ideas, often using one member's idea as a spring board for additional ideas. One person can be the recorder and write all ideas as they are given on a large piece of paper or each person can be given a pad of self-stick removable notes on which to write ideas. If this second way of recording ideas is used, you will need to take some time after the brainstorming session to organize all the ideas on a written list. The rules for brainstorming are as follows:

Rules for Brainstorming
1. **Go for quantity** - Write down as many ideas as possible.
2. **Let fantasy rule** - Write down all ideas, even the wild and crazy ones. They may trigger other, more useful ideas.
3. **No Criticism** - Judgement comes later, in the Judging Ideas phase. At this point, all ideas are accepted.
4. **Piggy-backing is encouraged** - Use other people's ideas as a stimulus for your ideas. It's acceptable to elaborate on other people's ideas.

3. Forced Relationships

One technique for stimulating ideas is to use another, unrelated item and relate that item to the problem. The outside stimulus could be something chosen at random from a dictionary or catalog, something you see when looking out the window, or something you find when thumbing through an encyclopedia. Choose an item and ask, "What ideas do I get about solving this problem by thinking about this object?"

An example might be if you were trying to think of ways to improve the classroom chair and had selected a paper clip, tree, and garden hose for forced relationships. Your thought process might lead to the following ideas:

paper clip
- make it out of metal
- have an apparatus to keep papers in place
- make it spring loaded it so it can be adjusted for larger bodies

tree
- give it something that will shade the person using it
- make each one different
- root it into the floor so it won't tip over

garden hose
- make it flexible
- make it portable
- hook up to water and electricity

Give students a sample problem to practice this technique. Choose one of the following problems or improvement situations. Then randomly select three objects for a forced relationship. After students have worked for a few minutes brainstorming ideas, ask them to consider each object in relationship to their problem. What new ideas does this object make them think of?

Practice problems:
- You want to quit biting your nails.
- How can you improve a shovel?
- In what ways might you show someone you care?
- How can you help with the homeless problem in your community?
- What can you do to earn more money?
- How can you improve a common pencil?

4. Idea Checklist

Another way to spur ideas is to use an idea checklist. This is a list of words (usually verbs) that are related to the problem by asking, "What can you (verb)?" You can use any list of words or questions, but the most common ones are *simplify, substitute, adapt, modify, magnify, minify, put to other uses, eliminate, reverse, rearrange, subtract, combine,* or *add*.

Tell students that certain key words can be used to help generate ideas. When they are looking for creative ideas, they can use these idea-spurring words by thinking about each word and asking how it relates to their problem.

Provide an example of someone who is trying to improve a toothbrush. By using the following words, they may come up with these ideas (some of which have been actual changes to the common toothbrush):

break in into parts - make it fold or collapse so travelers can easily pack it, make the head interchangeable

add to it - add flavors, colored bristles, motion, a small mirror

combination - combine with a stream of water, combine with floss dispenser, combine with shaving razor

substitute - make from a pliable material

magnify - add a row of bristles, put bristles on both ends, make the handle larger

minify - make smaller for children or to get into small spaces

Apply the idea-spurring words to the following problem:

You are a manufacturer of bags and want to expand your business. You have the capability of making bags in any size, shape or material. You want to think of how people would use these bags because if there is a potential use for a certain type of bag, you can manufacture it and sell it to people. What are all the uses for bags?

5. Interlude Brainstorming

Interlude brainstorming is similar to forced relationships. It begins with regular brainstorming but after a period of time, participants stop, experience a stimulus that is unrelated to the problem, write down the impressions or feelings they get from the stimulus, and finally apply the stimulus words to the problem to see what new solutions that suggests.

Give students a problem or use a problem on which they are presently working. Have students work in groups to brainstorm solutions or ideas for improvement.

After they have worked for a period of time that will allow them to generate a fair amount of ideas, have them stop. Provide another stimulus (a large picture, picture that is projected on the board so everyone can see it, or a short selection of music or sounds).

After students have looked at the picture or listened to the sounds for a minute or two, ask them to write down the impressions they got from the experience.

Then have them go back to their problem and use the words generated by the picture or sounds to spur ideas for solving the problem by considering each word in relation to the problem.

6. Attribute Listing

Another idea-spurring technique is to list the attributes of the problem and then consider each characteristic separately and ask, "What ideas do I have for improving this component or solving this part of the problem?" This technique is particularly useful for multifaceted problems or for improving objects that have several components. For instance, if you were looking for ways to improve shoes, you might consider the following parts: material, sole, upper portion, fastener. You could then look for ideas for improving each of these parts.

If you want your students to practice this technique, use one of the following problems. For each one, list the major parts or components and then for each one look for improvements.

- Design a new cereal for that would appeal to 40-year olds.
- What are all the ways to improve umbrellas?
- Create a new candy bar.
- What are some ideas for making a better calendar?
- How can you improve shoes?
- Propose changes for a bicycle.
- Design a new board game.
- Suggest changes for the water fountains in your school.

Name _____

Attention! Attention!

Bret wants to get the attention of a certain girl who sits across the room from him. How might he do this? List as many ideas as possible.

_____

_____

_____

_____

_____

_____

_____

_____

_____

_____

_____

Put a * by your five best ideas.

© 1994 Dandy Lion - C.P.S. for Kids

Name _____

Peanut Butter Problem

You have just won 50 kilograms of peanut butter. While you really like peanut butter, there is a limit to the number of peanut butter and jelly sandwiches you can eat. What are some unconventional uses for all this peanut butter? List as many ideas as you can.

_____

_____

_____

_____

_____

_____

_____

_____

_____

_____

Put a * by your five best ideas.

© 1994 Dandy Lion - C. P. S. for Kids

Name _____

Brainstorming

My problem is _____

Make a long list of all the ideas you can for solving your problem.

_____

_____

_____

_____

_____

_____

_____

_____

_____

_____

_____

_____

_____

_____

_____

_____

_____

_____

Put a * by the ideas that are the strongest.

© 1994 Dandy Lion - C.P.S. for Kids

Name _____

Mind Jogger

When you need a few good ideas but cannot think of anything, you can use catalogs and magazines to jog your thought process. Just open up a catalog, newspaper or magazine and look at the pictures and headlines. As you do, ask yourself, "What ideas does this give me for solving my problem?" Write down all the ideas — even the crazy ones.

Problem_____

_____

Ideas I got from looking through_____.

_____

_____

_____

_____

_____

_____

_____

_____

_____

_____

Put a * by the best ideas.

© 1994 Dandy Lion - C. P. S. for Kids

Name _____

Attribute Listing

List all the characteristics, features or attributes of the thing you are trying to improve. Then think of ways to improve or change each feature.

Characteristics   **Ideas for changes or improvements**

_____   _____

_____   _____

_____   _____

_____   _____

_____   _____

_____   _____

_____   _____

_____   _____

_____   _____

Put a * by your best ideas.

© 1994 Dandy Lion - C.P.S. for Kids

Name _____

Idea Wheel

Write your problem in the center of the wheel. Use the words in each section to help you think of ideas for solving the problem.

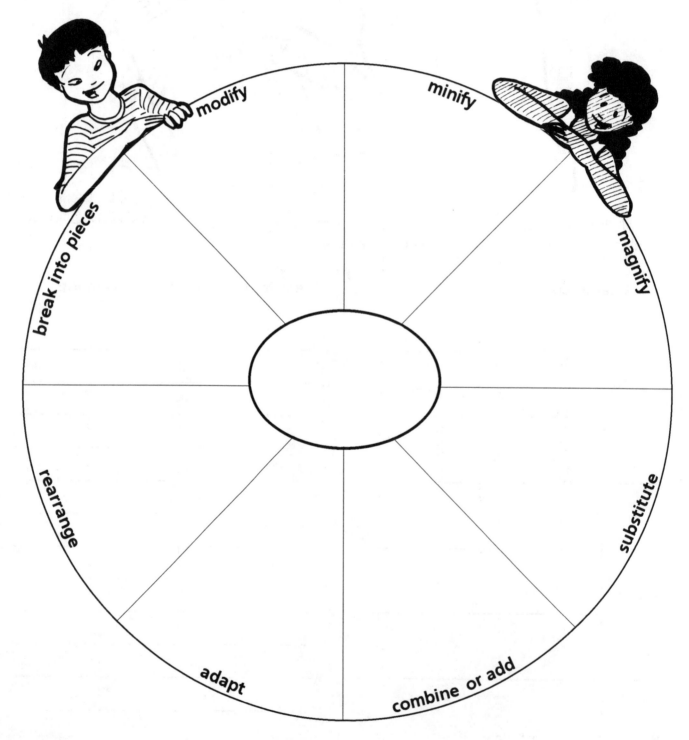

  © 1994 Dandy Lion - C. P. S. for Kids

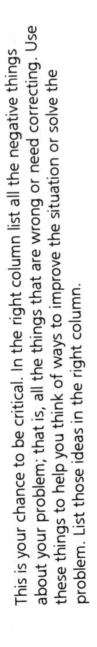

What's Wrong Brainstorming

Name _____

This is your chance to be critical. In the right column list all the negative things about your problem; that is, all the things that are wrong or need correcting. Use these things to help you think of ways to improve the situation or solve the problem. List those ideas in the right column.

Problem _____

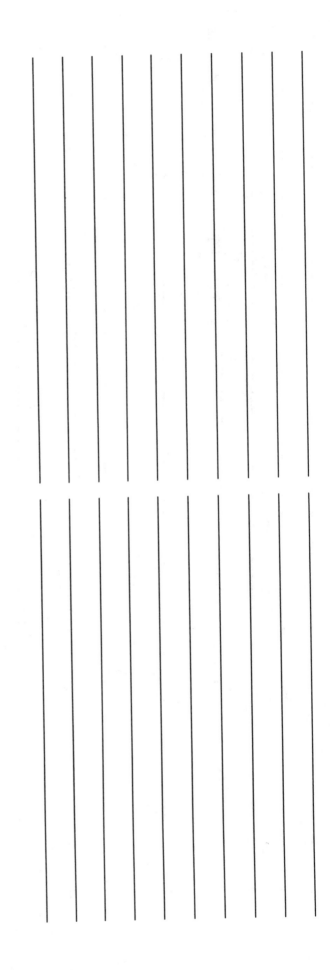

What's Wrong

Solution Ideas

© 1994 Dandy Lion - C.P.S. for Kids

Name _____

Finding Similarities

By comparing your problem to other things, you can sometimes come up with more creative ideas for a solution. Use this page to compare your problem to other things and then to record all the ideas this comparison makes you think of.

Problem _____

Think about how your problem is like a _____. What ideas does this give you?

_____

_____

Think about how your problem is like a _____. What ideas does this give you?

_____

_____

Think about how your problem is like a _____. What ideas does this give you?

_____

_____

© 1994 Dandy Lion - C. P. S. for Kids

Teaching notes
Judging Ideas

At this point, after generating a large pool of possible solutions in the Finding Ideas stage, students will use criteria to select the one best idea. The criteria are standards or measures used to judge an idea's usefulness. These standards are used systematically to analyze all the solutions that were generated and to select the most promising idea(s).

The first step in this phase of problem solving is to select three to five criteria for screening options. Point out to students that criteria change, and criteria for one situation or one time may not be the criteria they would choose at a different time or for a different situation. To select criteria, one might consider the following:

1. usefulness in accomplishing the objective
2. effects on people
3. effects on costs or time
4. effects on tangible things — materials, equipment, tools
5. effects on intangible things — opinions, attitudes, values, relationships, time
6. feasibility or difficulty in implementing
7. consequences

Once students have selected the criteria, they will use these standards to rate each idea. The most typical and systematic way to do this is to make a grid with the ideas for evaluation listed on one side and the criteria listed along the top. All ideas should be evaluated using a single criterion before evaluating the ideas with a second criterion. There are various ways of marking the appropriateness of each idea in relationship to each criterion. Some of the most common ways are:

A, B, C, D
1 (low) to 5 (high)
+ √ —
☺ ☺ ☹

Questions

Once the rating has been completed, students will select the idea(s) that they feel best solves the problem. Before selecting the one best idea, they should ask the following:

1. How do you know if this is a good idea?
2. What test must a good solution pass?
3. Is there one idea that is the best?
4. Are there two ideas that could be combined to make one great idea?
5. Which idea(s) can you use now? Which ideas do you want to hold and use at a later time? Which ideas do you want to modify? Which ideas do you want to reject?
6. Can you change any of the ideas to make them more usable?
7. Are some of the criteria more important than others? If so, how does this change the selection?

Lessons and Teaching Suggestions

1. Cookie Criteria

Ask students to consider what makes a good chocolate chip cookie. List all of the ideas that are given and then select the three to five criteria that they agree are the best "tests" for determining a good cookie.

Bring in a couple of different kinds of cookies and evaluate the cookies using the criteria you selected. Make a grid that lists the types or brands of cookies down the left side and the criteria along the top. Decide on a way of marking the grid and then have students rate the cookies either individually or in small groups.

2. Toy Criteria

Tell students to pretend that they have $20 to buy a toy for a younger sibling. Ask them to individually list criteria for the new toy they will buy. Remind them that they are thinking of criteria (ways of judging a good toy), and should not be swayed by any one particular toy. Then give them a list of five different popular toys and have them rate each toy using their own criteria.

3. A Friend's Gift

Ask students to pretend that they are going shopping for a birthday present for their best friend. Ask them to write down four different criteria or standards for selecting the perfect gift.

4. Pros and Cons

When students have only a couple of solutions from which to choose, it is useful to examine the pros and cons of each idea. To do this, positive and negative aspects of each solution are listed. If some of the positive or negative aspects are more important than others, these should be highlighted. You can then put the solutions and their pros and cons next to each other and select the solution that is strongest or has the most positive aspects and the least negative aspects.

5. Rank Order

An alternate way to judge solutions is to use the rank order method. Six to eight solutions are selected from the Finding Ideas phase. The solutions are then compared against each other, two at a time, and the best of the two is selected for a second round of evaluation. If a solution is eliminated when it is compared to one of the choices but it is strong enough to remain in the running, it can be placed on the bottom of the chart and compared to another rejected idea. The comparison continues until all other solutions have been eliminated and the best solution remains.

An example might be what to do on a Saturday night. The choices are listed as follows:

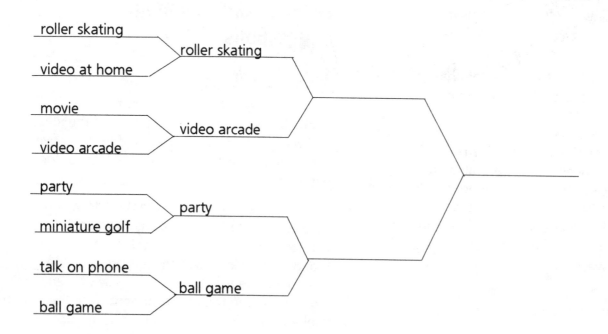

Name _____

New Car

When people purchase a new car, they have many different ideas about what makes the perfect car. Here is a list of some of the criteria that people use. Choose the five most important things you would want in a car. Then ask an older person to select five criteria.

1. Made in our country
2. Dependable; doesn't break down often
3. Powerful engine
4. Easy to maneuver and park
5. Fuel efficient
6. Big trunk or other space for hauling things
7. Spacious interior
8. Comfortable seats
9. Built well
10. Color

11. Sporty styling
12. Solid highway handling
13. Good radio
14. Cost
15. Can carry ski equipment
16. Good warranty

My five most important criteria when choosing a car are _____

_____   _____

_____   _____

_____'s most important criteria when choosing a car are _____

_____   _____

_____   _____

© 1994 Dandy Lion - C.P.S. for Kids

Name _____

Judging Books

They say that you should never judge a book by its cover. But then how do you judge a good book? What do you think makes a good book? List four criteria for a good book.

1. _____

   _____

2. _____

   _____

3. _____

   _____

4. _____

   _____

Use your criteria to judge a book you have recently read. Write a paragraph telling why the book was good or why it was not good.

_____

_____

_____

_____

_____

_____

_____

© 1994 Dandy Lion - C. P. S. for Kids

Name _____

Feet Warming Ideas

Carol always has cold feet when she is at work. She hates having cold feet. She has made a list of ideas for solving this problem. She also has three criteria for a good solution. The criteria are:

1. It cannot cost her employer a lot of extra money.
2. It must not take a lot of time away from her job.
3. She must look professional to all the people who come into the office.

Use these criteria to judge each idea. Put a +, √, or – on the blanks in front of each idea.

1   2   3

___ ___ ___ Wear thick wool socks

___ ___ ___ Get electric socks

___ ___ ___ Wrap feet in a blanket

___ ___ ___ Take two pairs of shoes to work and every half an hour alternate warming a pair over the heater and wearing a warm pair of shoes

___ ___ ___ Move her desk closer to the heater so she can put her feet on the heater every now and then

___ ___ ___ Wear two pairs of socks

___ ___ ___ Forget fashion and wear ugly but warm shoes or boots

___ ___ ___ Put an electric warming device under her desk so she can put her feet on it

___ ___ ___ Get exercise to raise natural body heat

___ ___ ___ Wear warm slippers

___ ___ ___ Raise her feet above her waist by putting her feet up on her desk

___ ___ ___ Do foot exercises to get blood flowing to the feet

___ ___ ___ Put her feet in a warm water bath every half an hour

___ ___ ___ Quit this job and get a job in the tropics

Name _____

Using a Criteria Grid

Chose your five best ideas for solving your problem. Write them along the left side of the grid. Choose three to five criteria for judging the best solution. Write them along the top of the grid. Then judge each idea with each criterion. If an idea rates high, write a **3** in the space. Write a **2** if it rates okay, and write a **1** if it rates poorly. Do this for all ideas.

Solution Ideas	Criteria						keep	hold	reject

The best solution would be to _____

© 1994 Dandy Lion - C. P. S. for Kids

Judging Ideas

Name _____

Rank Order

Write your best solutions on the lines below. Consider each group of two ideas and decide which of the two solutions is better. Write that solution on the line to the right. If there is an idea that is not as good as the one it is being paired, with but is too good to be eliminated, write it below the other ideas. Keep comparing and eliminating ideas until you have the best solution.

1.

2.

3.

4.

5.

6.

7.

8.

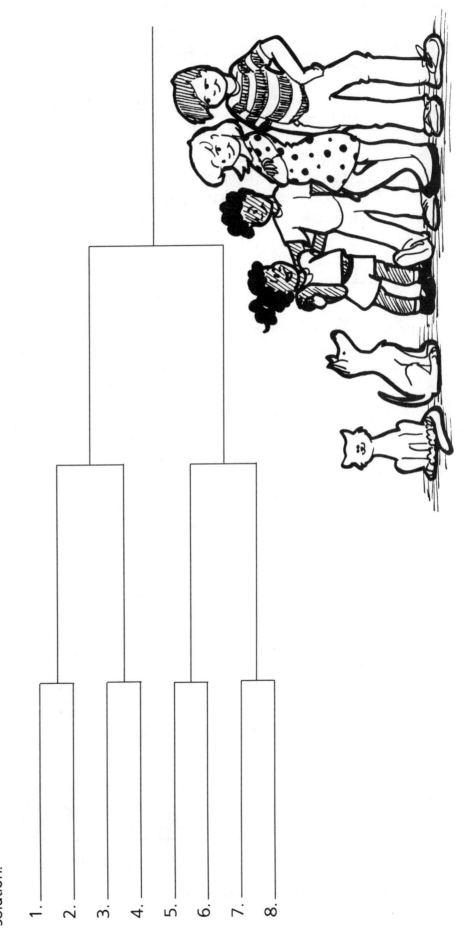

© 1994 Dandy Lion - C.P.S. for Kids

Name _____

How Does It Measure Up?

Choose your five best ideas from your brainstorming session and number them 1 through 5. Then choose criteria by which to judge the ideas. Write each criterion on a scale below. Then decide how well each idea measures up against each criterion. Place the number of the idea on the appropriate place on the rating scale.

great   Criterion _____   poor

great   Criterion _____   poor

great   Criterion _____   poor

great   Criterion _____   poor

great   Criterion _____   poor

Choose the idea that has the best overall rating.

© 1994 Dandy Lion - C. P. S. for Kids

Name _____

Pros and Cons

Select the four best ideas. For each idea, analyze the pros (the good things) and the cons (the bad or negative things) about each possible course of action.

Idea_____

Pros	Cons
_____	_____
_____	_____
_____	_____
_____	_____
_____	_____
_____	_____
_____	_____

Idea_____

Pros	Cons
_____	_____
_____	_____
_____	_____
_____	_____
_____	_____
_____	_____
_____	_____

Idea_____

Pros	Cons
_____	_____
_____	_____
_____	_____
_____	_____
_____	_____
_____	_____
_____	_____

Idea_____

Pros	Cons
_____	_____
_____	_____
_____	_____
_____	_____
_____	_____
_____	_____
_____	_____

After you have looked at the pros and cons, choose the best idea.

© 1994 Dandy Lion - C.P.S. for Kids

Taking Action

The final phase in Creative Problem Solving is to implement the solution that was selected in the Judging Ideas phase. To do this, students must consider those things that will either help or hinder their efforts and then make a plan to put the solution in action. They first identify sources of assistance and sources of resistance (people, things, customs). Then they must determine what they have to do to put their solution in action. For solutions that involve several steps, they should designate one thing that they will do immediately, a few short-term actions and several long-term goals. Along with the obvious actions they should consider people they need to talk to or write to, information they need to get, permissions they need to secure, public relations (speeches, news releases, etc.) they need to generate, and thank yous they need to send — all those things that will make the difference between their project soaring to success or gliding to half-completed disappointment.

Questions

The appropriate questions to ask at this stage are:

1. What needs to be done?
2. When does it have to be done?
3. Where do I start?
4. Can I break it down into smaller tasks?
5. What can be done right away?
6. What can be done later?
7. Are there any problems?
8. What could go wrong?
9. Who can help?
10. Who needs to give their approval?
11. Who needs to be "sold" on the idea?
12. How will I know if I succeeded?
13. Once I've accomplished my goal, what do I do next?

Lessons and Teaching Suggestions

1. Easy Versus Complex Action Plans

Discuss with students the fact that once a solution has been selected, they then have to do whatever they decided to do. Sometimes the appropriate action is simple (like buying a greeting card) and sometimes it is complex and will take a long time and several steps to implement (like starting a student newspaper).

Give students the following actions and have them rate them on a scale of 1 to 3 with 1 being easy, short-term and 3 being complex, long-term.

- telling a friend you are sorry
- buying a new suit
- running for a class office
- campaigning for an end to pollution by a local manufacturing company
- painting a landscape
- painting a landscape if you don't know how to paint

2. New Pet

As a group consider the situation of a person who has decided to get a new puppy. Make a list of obstacles and sources of help. Then outline the steps the person must take. Note which action he or she will take immediately.

3. Park Plans

Pretend that your class has decided to turn a vacant lot in the neighborhood into a park. Make a list of any possible concerns and where the class can find help for its project. Then list the steps the class would take from the beginning to the end of this project.

© 1994 Dandy Lion - C. P. S. for Kids

Name _____

Noisy Hobby

Choose one of the following activities.
- learn to play the drums
- learn to tap dance
- learn to sing
- learn karate

Pretend that you have decided to take up this activity. Your mother has given you her permission to do this. You live in an apartment building on the second floor. This is an old building with little sound insulation between apartments. Plan how you will implement your decision.

What problems might you encounter? _____

_____

Where could you get help? _____

_____

Number the following tasks to indicate the order in which the tasks should be completed.

_____ Sign up for classes

_____ Send out invitations to your first performance or demonstration

_____ Practice half an hour every day

_____ Get equipment, gear, clothing

_____ Inform neighbors of your plan to see if they have any objections or concerns

_____ Get permission from your parents

_____ Call and get information about classes and prices

What are two other things you would need to do?

_____

_____

Name _____

A Caring Project

Stella wants to do something to help other people. After a lot of thinking, she has decided to collect old teddy bears, recondition them and give them to children in hospitals. She has made a list of things that she needs to do to make this project a reality. Help her organize her list by numbering the tasks to show the order in which they should be completed.

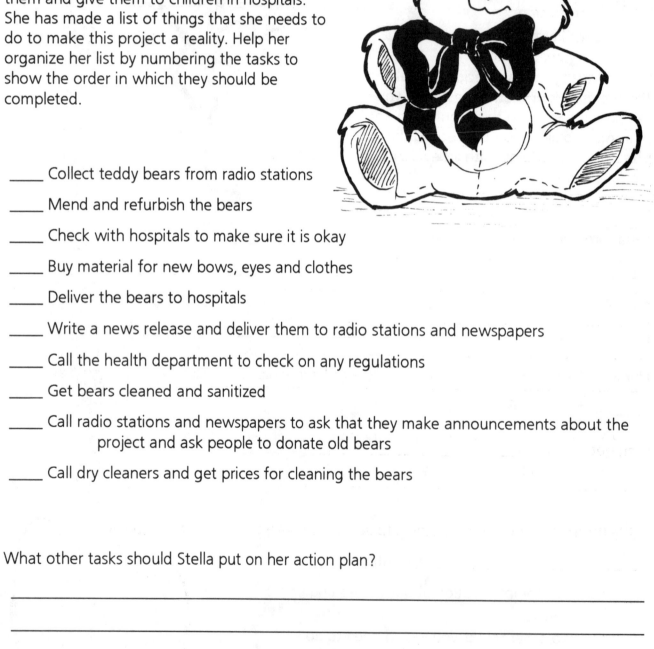

_____ Collect teddy bears from radio stations

_____ Mend and refurbish the bears

_____ Check with hospitals to make sure it is okay

_____ Buy material for new bows, eyes and clothes

_____ Deliver the bears to hospitals

_____ Write a news release and deliver them to radio stations and newspapers

_____ Call the health department to check on any regulations

_____ Get bears cleaned and sanitized

_____ Call radio stations and newspapers to ask that they make announcements about the project and ask people to donate old bears

_____ Call dry cleaners and get prices for cleaning the bears

What other tasks should Stella put on her action plan?

_____

_____

_____

_____

© 1994 Dandy Lion - C. P. S. for Kids

Name _____

Time Line

Devise a plan for doing those things that will solve your problem. Make a schedule of what you will do and when you will do it. Check off each task as it is completed.

My solution is_____

Things I need to do	Do by	✓

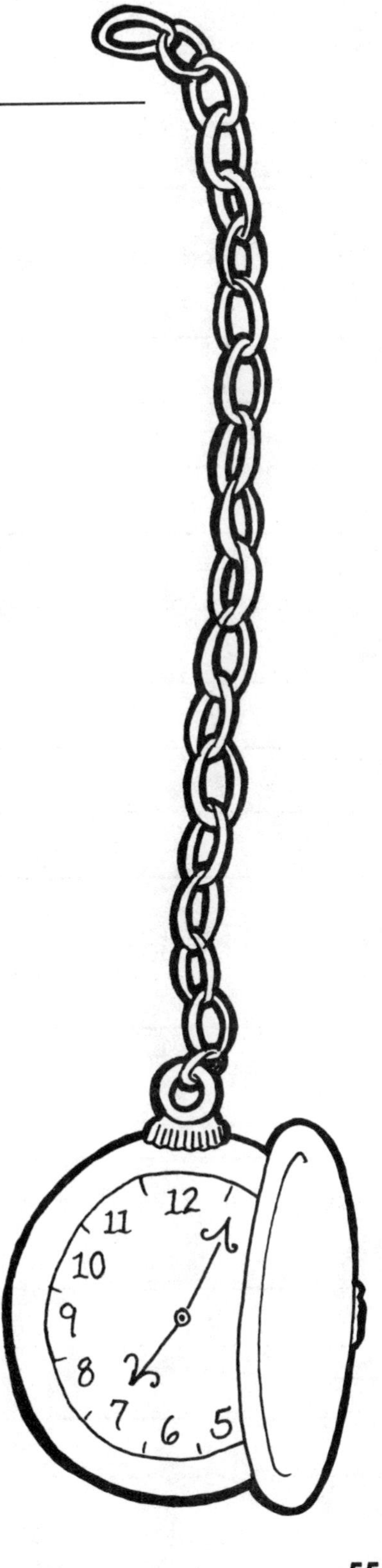

I can get help from _____

_____

Problems I might encounter _____

_____

_____

_____

_____

Name _____

Selling Your Idea

Develop a plan for selling your problem solution.

The solution is_____

_____

_____

People I need to convince

_____

_____

_____

_____

The benefits or advantages of accepting this idea

_____

_____

_____

_____

Possible objections

_____

_____

_____

How to overcome the objections

_____

_____

_____

_____

_____

_____

© 1994 Dandy Lion - C. P. S. for Kids

Name _____

Plan of Action

Solution _____

Get help from _____
_____

Things to do immediately _____
_____

Things to do later _____

_____

_____

_____

_____

_____

Things that might go wrong_____

_____

Name _____

Christmas Gifts

Dora has three close friends. They do everything together. They often spend the night at each others' houses. She would like to give them a small gift at Christmas to let them know how much their friendship means to her. She only has $3.00, which she knows is not enough money to buy three gifts. Christmas is two weeks away. She can earn $5.00 a week by cleaning and ironing for her grandmother, but her grandmother doesn't pay her until the end of the month when she gets her retirement check. She would not have the money in time to buy a gift. Dora does not have a credit card. One of Dora's friend's father owns the local drug store. Another friend has a family that is very wealthy. Dora does not know if her friends will give her a gift, and she doesn't really expect anything. She would, however, feel embarrassed if one of her friends gave her a gift and she didn't have anything to give her. If Dora does get a gift, she hopes it is red. Red is her favorite color. She hates purple. Dora's younger brother has $50.00, but he is saving for a guitar and will not open his bank until he has enough money to buy the guitar. Dora and her brother fight a lot. Dora's mother likes Dora's friends, but she will not loan Dora the money because she wants her to learn to manage her money better. Dora will turn 12 years old on December 27th. Dora is a good artist but a poor baseball player.

Underline the most important facts that tell about Dora's problem.

　　　　　　　　　　　　　　　　　　　© 1994 Dandy Lion - C. P. S. for Kids

Name _____

Christmas Gifts

Dora wants to give Christmas presents to her friends, but she doesn't have enough money to buy the gifts. Read all the important facts about Dora and her problem. Then think about what the "real problem" might be. Write as many ideas as you can by completing this sentence in many different ways.

1. In what ways might Dora _____

2. In what ways might Dora _____

3. In what ways might Dora _____

4. In what ways might Dora _____

5. In what ways might Dora _____

6. In what ways might Dora _____

7. In what ways might Dora _____

8. In what ways might Dora _____

9. In what ways might Dora _____

10. In what ways might Dora_____

Choose the statement that you think best describes the problem.

The real problem is _____

Name _____

Christmas Gifts

Dora's real problem is _____

What are all the things Dora could do to solve her problem? Think of a lot of creative ideas.
Write as many ideas as you can.

1. _____
2. _____
3. _____
4. _____
5. _____
6. _____
7. _____
8. _____
9. _____
10. _____
11. _____
12. _____
13. _____
14. _____
15. _____

If you have more ideas, write them on the back of this sheet of paper.

Put a * by the ideas you think are the best.

                                     © 1994 Dandy Lion - C. P. S. for Kids

Name _____

Christmas Gifts

Now that you have made a long list of ideas for Dora, you need to choose the best idea. To do this, you must measure one idea against the others. This is a list of criteria that Dora might use to select the best solution to her problem.

1. The solution must be able to be implemented within 12 days.
2. All friends should receive something of equal value.
3. The gifts should not appear cheap.
4. The solution must be honest.
5. The solution should be something her friends would like.

List your best ideas and rate how each one meets the criteria. Use this way of rating.

☺ = very good   😐 = okay   ☹ = not very good

Ideas	12 days	equal	not cheap	honest	like

Look at each idea and its ratings. Choose the idea that you think is the best.

My choice for the best solution is_____

_____

Name _____

Christmas Gifts

Now it is time for Dora to put her solution into action. Help her get started by listing the things she has to do.

Plan of Action

Get help from _____

_____

Talk to _____

_____

Things to do now _____

_____

_____

_____

_____

Things to do later _____

_____

_____

_____

Things that might go wrong _____

_____

                                    © 1994 Dandy Lion - C. P. S. for Kids

Name _____

Basketball Team

Josh is a great basketball player. He is very tall for his age. He has been playing basketball since he could hold a ball. He played on the junior varsity team last year and was one of the highest scoring players. He has gone to basketball camp every summer for the last four summers. He even played in a tournament where the players were selected from the best players in the state. His team won. He knew that he would be selected to play on the varsity team this year. The school's basketball team is not very good. They have lost most of their games for the last 10 years. They have had the same coach for all those years. Josh's mother made a comment to someone that she was disappointed with the basketball program. She thought they should retire the coach and get someone better. The coach found out what she said and got very upset about it. The try-outs for basketball were yesterday. Today the list of players was posted. Josh's name was not on the list. Many of the boys who were selected for the team were not as good as Josh. Josh feels that he is being punished for something his mother did. Josh is disappointed and mad. Josh's parents feel that he has not been treated fairly. Josh's best friend is on the team. Josh does not play football, but he does take part in track and swimming. He is very shy. Basketball games start in three weeks. The coach could add two more players to the team and still be within league guidelines for team size. The coach says that his decision was not based on any personal bias and it is final.

Underline the most important facts that tell about Josh's problem.

© 1994 Dandy Lion - C.P.S. for Kids

Name _____

Basketball Team

Josh feels that he should have been on the team. His mother said something that made the coach mad. He was not selected for the team. Read all the important facts about Josh's problem. Then think about what the "real problem" might be. List as many ideas as you can by finishing the following sentence in many different ways.

1. In what ways might _____

2. In what ways might _____

3. In what ways might _____

4. In what ways might _____

5. In what ways might _____

6. In what ways might _____

7. In what ways might _____

8. In what ways might _____

9. In what ways might _____

10. In what ways might _____

Choose the statement that you think best describes the problem.

The "real problem" is _____

                                    © 1994 Dandy Lion - C. P. S. for Kids

Name _____

Basketball Team

Josh's real problem is _____

_____

What are all the things Josh can do to solve his problem? Think of a lot of creative ideas. Write as many ideas as you can.

1. _____
2. _____
3. _____
4. _____
5. _____
6. _____
7. _____
8. _____
9. _____
10. _____
11. _____
12. _____
13. _____
14. _____
15. _____

If you have more ideas, write them on the back of this sheet of paper.

Put a * by the ideas you think are the best.

Name _____

Basketball Team

Now that you have made a long list of ideas for Josh, you need to choose the best idea. To do this, you must measure one idea against the others. This is a list of criteria that Josh has made to judge the list of ideas.

1. The solution cannot get him in trouble with his other teachers.
2. The solution should not draw a lot of attention to him from other students.
3. The solution should be fair to the other players.
4. The solution should show results within 3 weeks.
5.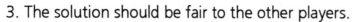

    (add your own criteria)

List your best ideas and rate how each one meets the criteria. Use this way of rating.

☺ = very good   ☺ = okay   ☹ = not very good

Ideas	**Criteria**				

My choice for the best solution is _____

                                    © 1994 Dandy Lion - C. P. S. for Kids

Name _____

Basketball Team

Now it is time for Josh to put his plan into action. Help him get started by listing everything he has to do.

The solution is _____

_____

_____

Things Josh needs to do _____

_____

_____

_____

_____

_____

_____

_____

People Josh could get help from _____

_____

_____

Problems Josh might encounter _____

_____

_____

Name _____

New School

   Chris's parents have just announced that they are moving in a month. This means that
he will have to leave Jefferson School one month before school is out for the summer and
attend a new school for one month. He will be graduating from Jefferson in June. He has
always attended Jefferson and has many friends there. He really likes his teacher this year. He
finds his classes interesting and enjoys being on the school baseball team. He is upset that he
has to leave all this. Their new home will be fifteen miles from their present home. It is in the
same city and the school is in the same school district. In fact, both Jefferson and the new
school feed into the same junior high, so Chris will see his old friends next year. Chris is
worried about having to make new friends at the new school. His best friend is Treavor. They
have been best friends since first grade. Treavor lives across the street. His parents assure
Chris that he will like the new house because it has a large yard, big rooms, and is close to a
park. Chris is the catcher on his baseball team. He has a very good batting average. Playing
baseball is very important to him. Chris's friends say they will give him a going-away party.

Underline the important facts in Chris's story. Are there any additional facts that you would
like to know that would help you solve the problem?

Name _____

New School

Chris does not want to leave his school and move to a new school when his parents move to their new house. Read all the facts about Chris and his problem. Then think about what the "real problem" might be. List as many ideas as you can by completing the following sentence in many different ways.

1. How can I _____

2. How can I _____

3. How can I _____

4. How can I _____

5. How can I _____

6. How can I _____

7. How can I _____

8. How can I _____

9. How can I _____

10. How can I _____

Choose the statement that you think best describes the problem.

The real problem is _____

Name _____

New School

Chris's real problem is _____

_____

_____

What are all the things he could do to solve his
problem? Think of a lot of creative ideas. Write
as many ideas as you can.

1. _____
2. _____
3. _____
4. _____
5. _____
6. _____
7. _____
8. _____
9. _____
10. _____
11. _____
12. _____
13. _____
14. _____
15. _____

If you have more ideas, write them on the back of this sheet of paper.
Put a * by the ideas you think are the best.

                        © 1994 Dandy Lion - C. P. S. for Kids

Name _____

New School

Now that you have made a long list of possible solutions for Chris, you need to analyze the ideas to select the best solution. Choose the four most promising ideas. For each one, list the pros and cons.

Idea _____

Pros	Cons
_____	_____
_____	_____
_____	_____
_____	_____
_____	_____
_____	_____

Idea _____

Pros	Cons
_____	_____
_____	_____
_____	_____
_____	_____
_____	_____
_____	_____

Idea _____

Pros	Cons
_____	_____
_____	_____
_____	_____
_____	_____
_____	_____
_____	_____

Idea _____

Pros	Cons
_____	_____
_____	_____
_____	_____
_____	_____
_____	_____
_____	_____

Based on this analysis, which idea seems to be the best? _____

© 1994 Dandy Lion - C.P.S. for Kids

Name _____

New School

Make a plan of action that will help Chris
implement the selected solution.

The solution is_____

_____

_____

Things Chris needs to do _____

_____

_____

_____

_____

_____

_____

_____

_____

People Chris might get help from _____

_____

_____

_____

Problems Chris might encounter _____

_____

_____

_____

© 1994 Dandy Lion - C. P. S. for Kids

Name _____

Make a Difference Day

   You just read in a magazine that in two weeks there will be a national Make a Difference Day. This is a day when people all over the country will do things that make a positive difference in their communities. You can do the project by yourself or as part of a group. You can do something for one person, for a family, for an organization or for the environment. The story said that you can write a description of your special project and the magazine will publish an article about the best projects. It will also donate money to a charity or community organization in your name. You and some of your friends decide that you would like to organize a project for your community.

Add additional facts about your community that will make this problem reflect the needs of your community.

_____

_____

_____

_____

_____

_____

_____

_____

_____

Name _____

Make a Difference Day

You and your friends have decided to make a difference for one day. Read all the facts you wrote about the needs of your community. Think about what the "real problem" might be. List as many ideas as you can by finishing the following sentence in many different ways.

1. In what ways might _____

2. In what ways might _____

3. In what ways might _____

4. In what ways might _____

5. In what ways might _____

6. In what ways might _____

7. In what ways might _____

8. In what ways might _____

9. In what ways might _____

10. In what ways might _____

Choose the statement that you think best describes the problem.

The problem is _____

                                    © 1994 Dandy Lion - C. P. S. for Kids

Name _____

Make a Difference Day

The problem can best be stated as _____

_____

_____

What are all the things you and your friends could do to solve this problem? Think of a lot of creative ideas. Write as many ideas as you can.

1._____
2._____
3._____
4._____
5._____
6._____
7._____
8._____
9._____
10. _____
11. _____
12. _____
13. _____
14. _____
15. _____

If you have more ideas, write them on the back of this sheet of paper.

Put a * by the ideas you think are the best.

© 1994 Dandy Lion - C.P.S. for Kids

Name _____

Make a Difference Day

Look at the ideas you have generated as solutions for your problem. Choose the eight best ideas. Write them on the lines below. Consider each group of two ideas and decide which of the two solutions is better. Write that solution on the line to the right. Keep comparing and eliminating ideas until you have the best solution.

1. _____
2. _____
3. _____
4. _____
5. _____
6. _____
7. _____
8. _____

                                         © 1994 Dandy Lion - C. P. S. for Kids

Name _____

Make a Difference Day

Use this sheet to make plans for your Make a Difference Day project.

The solution is _____

_____

Plan of Action

Things to do	Who?	When?

What could go wrong? _____

_____

Who can help? _____

_____

Pocket Problem Solver

Sensing Problems

If you don't have a problem to solve, start your search here. Think about what is bothering you, what needs improving, what needs changing and what obstacles you'd like to overcome. Record your thoughts.

Choose one problem area.

Finding Facts

Write everything you know about your problem area. Write feelings and questions as well as facts.

© 1994 Dandy Lion - C. P. S. for Kids

Finding Ideas

Problem _____

Brainstorm a large number of possible solutions for the problem.

_____
_____
_____
_____
_____
_____
_____
_____
_____
_____
_____
_____

Choose the four or five best ideas.

Defining the Problem

Try stating the problem in several different ways by completing the statement "In what ways might..." or "How can ..."

_____
_____
_____
_____
_____
_____
_____
_____
_____

Choose the statement that best describes the problem.

Judging Ideas

Choose criteria for judging the ideas. Rate each idea using each criterion.

The best solution is _____

Taking Action

Plan of Action - Things to do

Get help from _____

Possible problems _____

© 1994 Dandy Lion - C. P. S. for Kids